The Best Of

Distributed in the United Kingdom by
Music Sales Limited.

Printed in the United Kingdom by
Redwood Books, Trowbridge, Wiltshire.

The Best Of U2

Transcribed by Andy Aledort.
In order to provide a complete transcription of the album,
we've included both guitar and bass parts for each song.
The guitar parts are in the first section of the book, following the
Notation Guide. The bass parts are in the last section of the book.

Notation Guide.

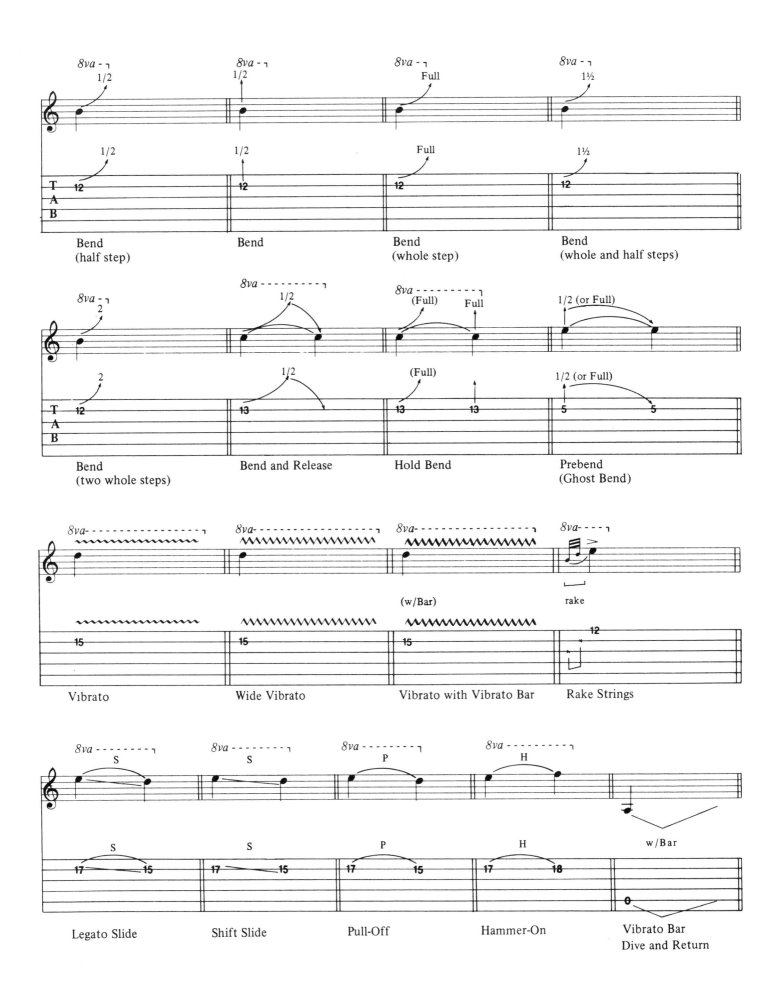

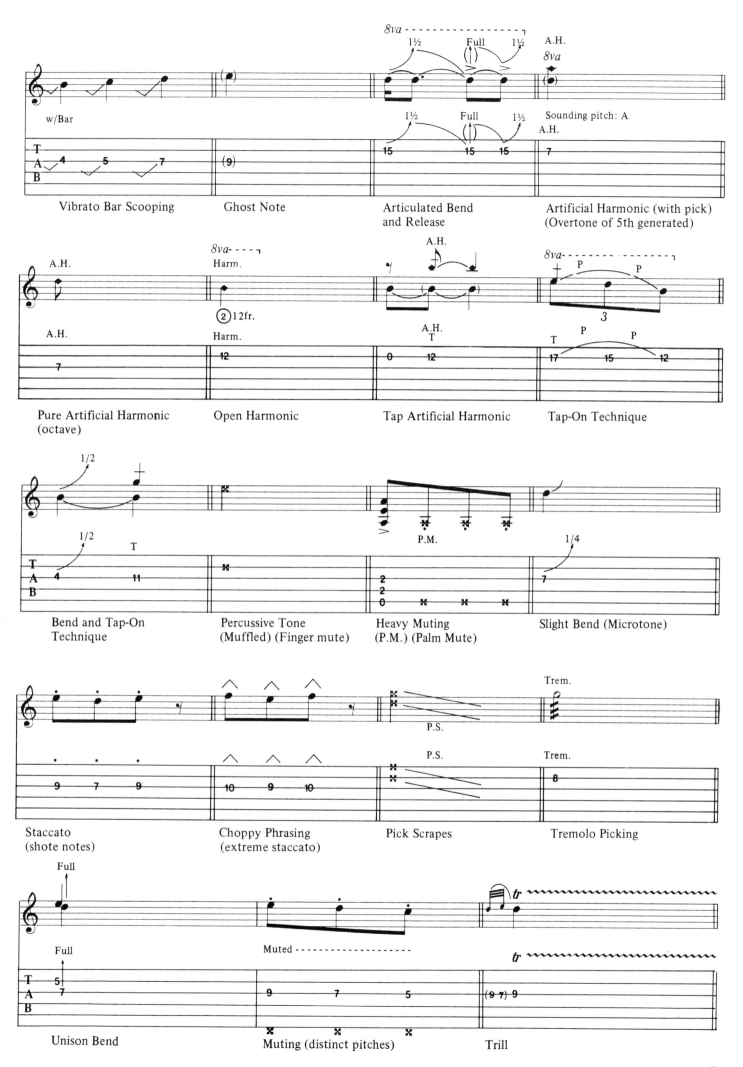

Vibrato Bar Scooping

Ghost Note

Articulated Bend and Release

Artificial Harmonic (with pick) (Overtone of 5th generated)

Pure Artificial Harmonic (octave)

Open Harmonic

Tap Artificial Harmonic

Tap-On Technique

Bend and Tap-On Technique

Percussive Tone (Muffled) (Finger mute)

Heavy Muting (P.M.) (Palm Mute)

Slight Bend (Microtone)

Staccato (shote notes)

Choppy Phrasing (extreme staccato)

Pick Scrapes

Tremolo Picking

Unison Bend

Muting (distinct pitches)

Trill

BAD

Words by BONO
Music by U2

Interlude

(Repeat on D.S. only)

11

GLORIA

Words by BONO
Music by U2

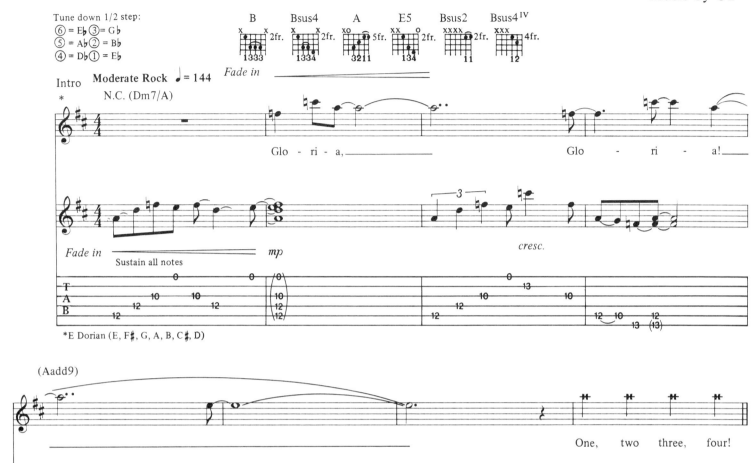

*E Dorian (E, F♯, G, A, B, C♯, D)

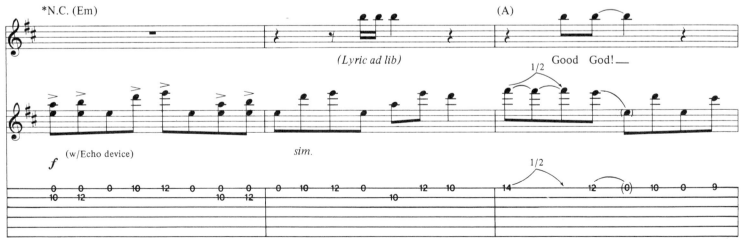

*Chord names derived from bass figure.

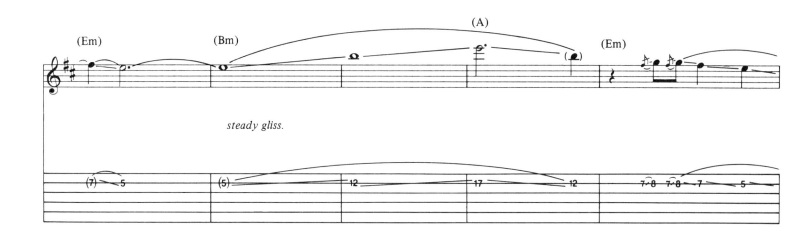

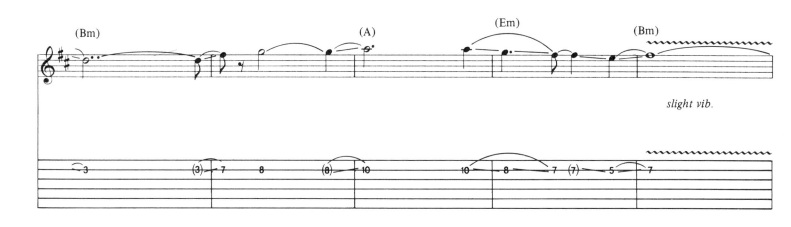

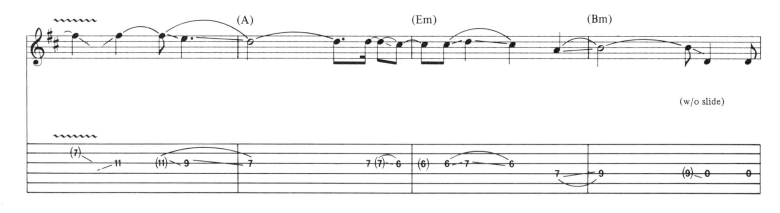

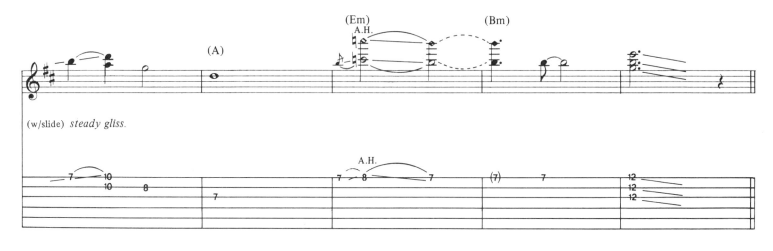

I WILL FOLLOW

*Slide past fretboard.

NEW YEARS DAY

Words by BONO
Music by U2

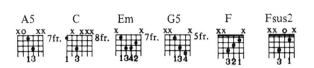

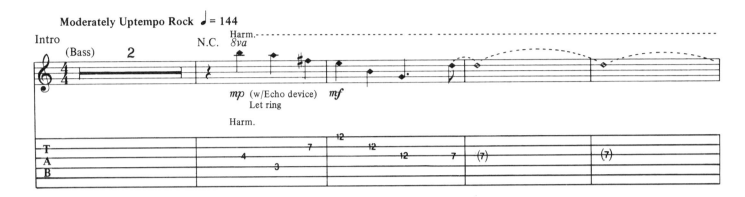

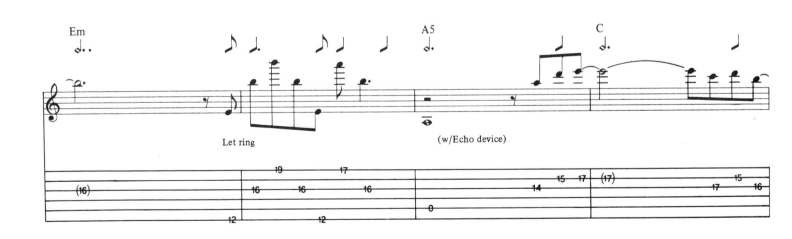

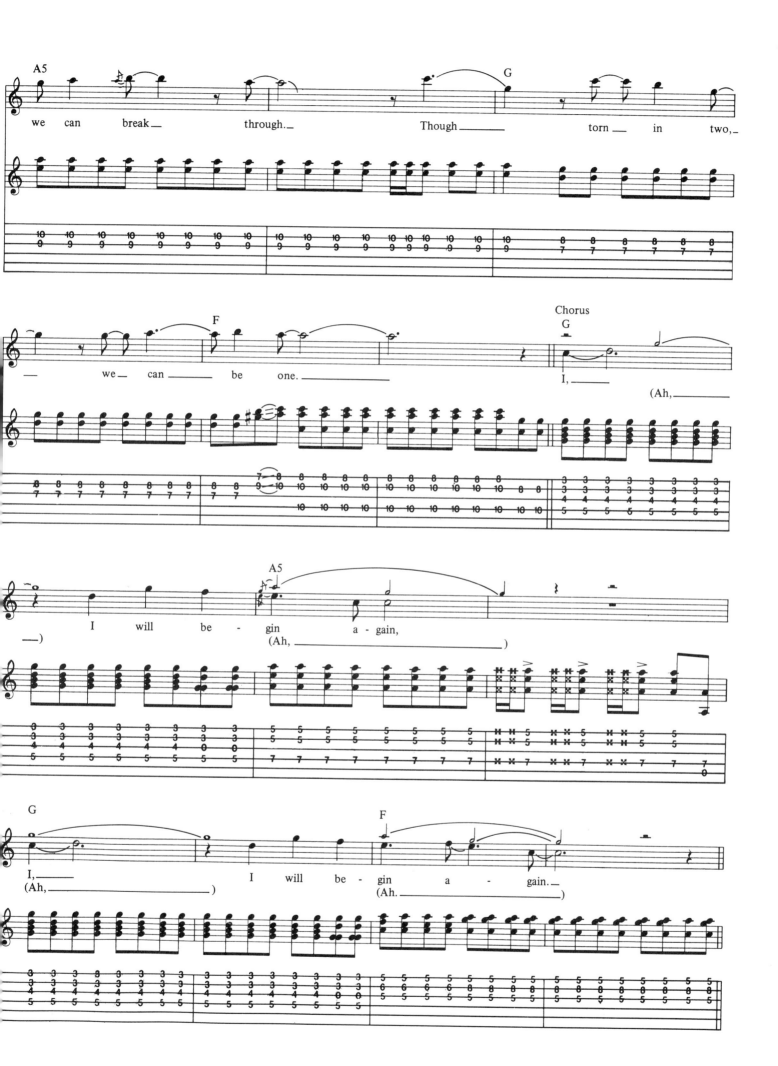

Interlude

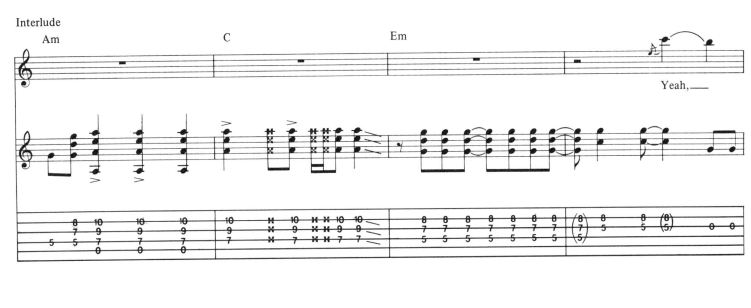

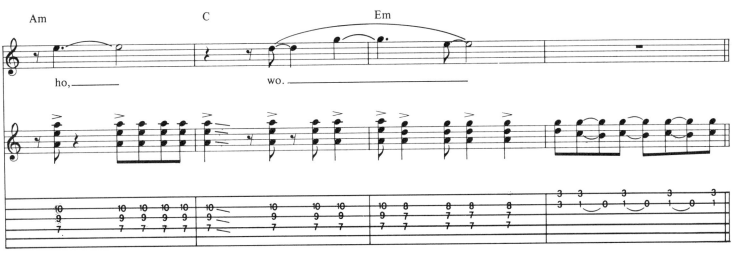

(Rhythm gtr. out)

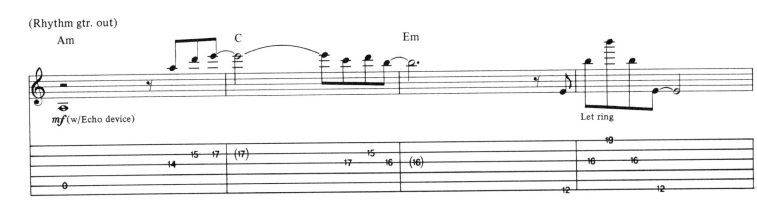

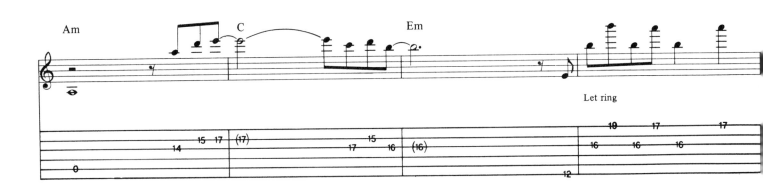

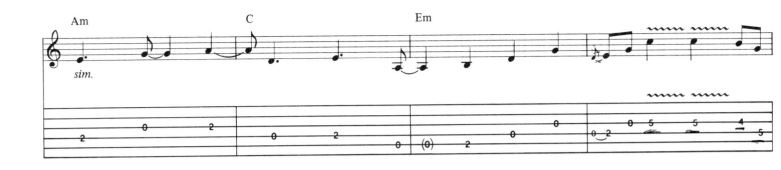

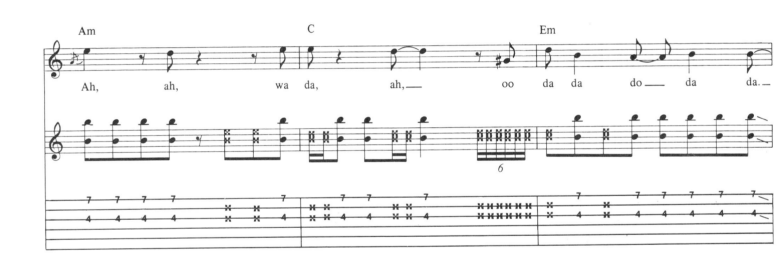

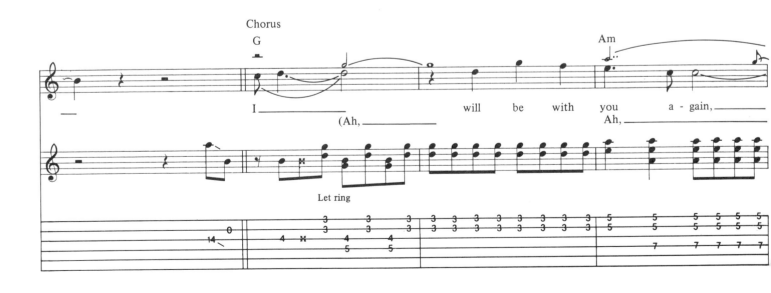

OCTOBER

Words by BONO
Music by U2

PRIDE
(IN THE NAME OF LOVE)

Words by BONO
Music by U2

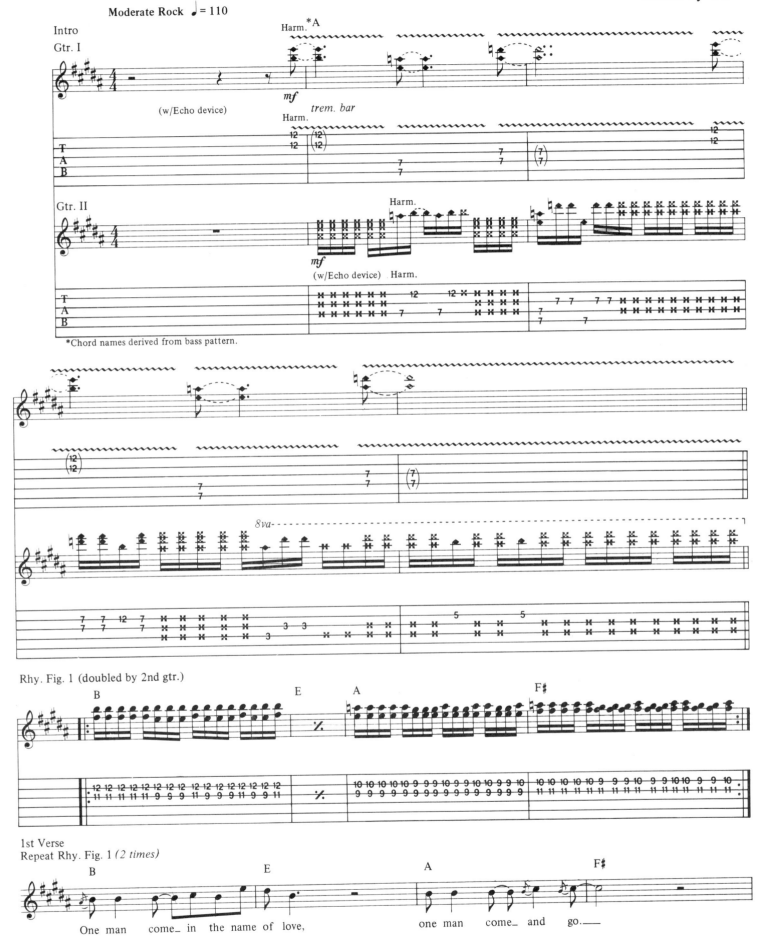

*Chord names derived from bass pattern.

Chorus
w/Rhy. Fig. 1 *(2 times)*

of love,_____ what more___ in the name of___ love.___ In the name___

of love,___ what more___ in the name of love.___

Interlude
w/Riff B *(2 times)*

Look out ___ for me.___ *(Lyric ad lib)*

Riff A

f

Repeat Riff A & Riff B *(6 times)*

Come back to me.

w/Rhy. Fig. 1 *(2 times)*
Riff C

sustain notes

Riff D

(sustain both notes)

Riff B

SUNDAY BLOODY SUNDAY

Words by BONO
Music by U2

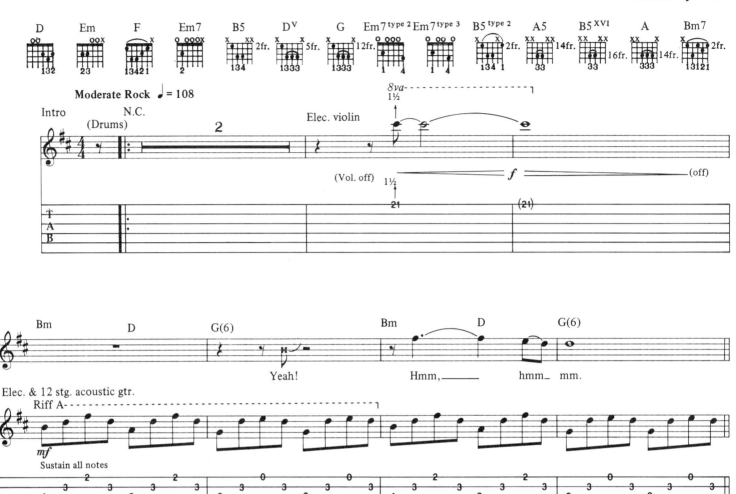

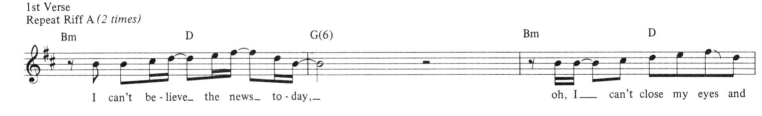

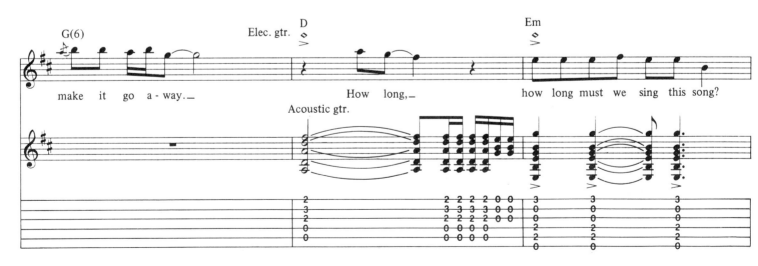

day. Oh, let's go.

How long, how long must we sing this song? How long, how

long? Ah! 'Cause to night Ah.

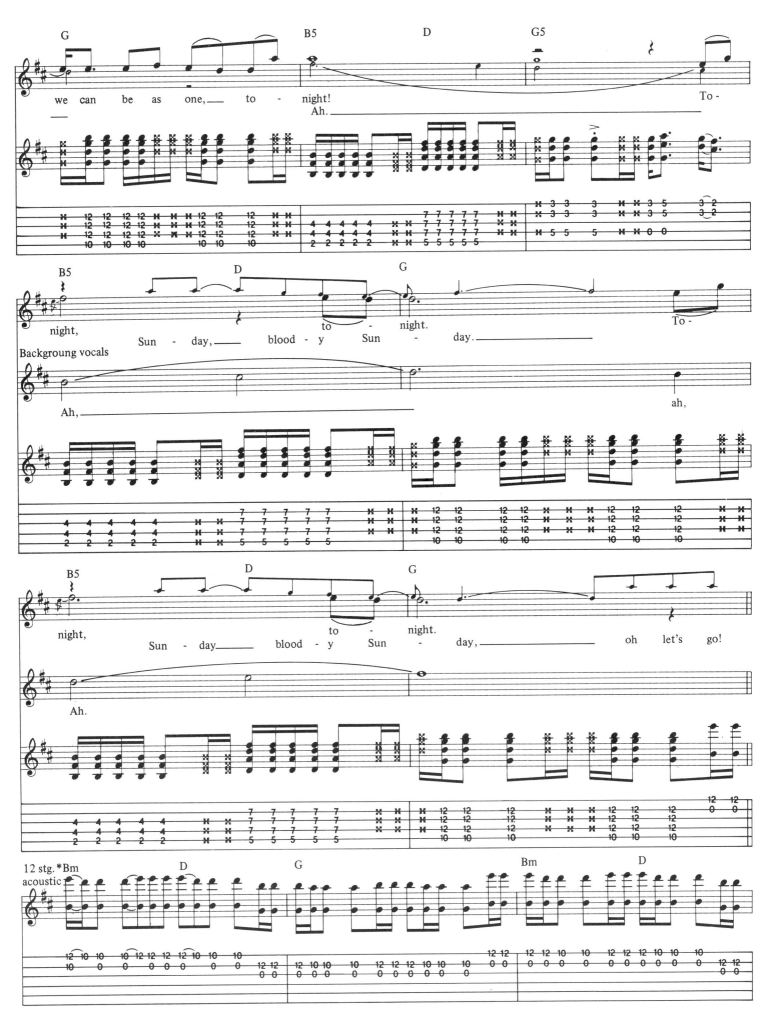

*Chord names derived from bass pattern.

SURRENDER

Words by BONO
Music by U2

*Past fretboard; sounds E

Sur - ren - der.
Sur - ren - der.

(Em7)

A SORT OF HOMECOMING

Words by BONO
Music by U2

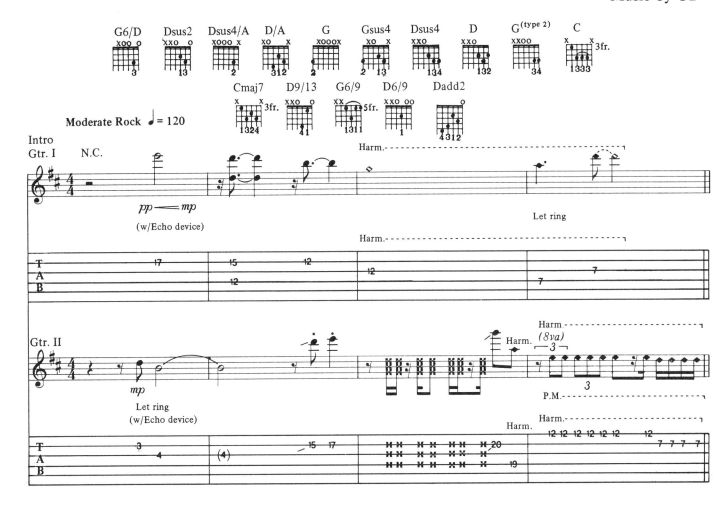

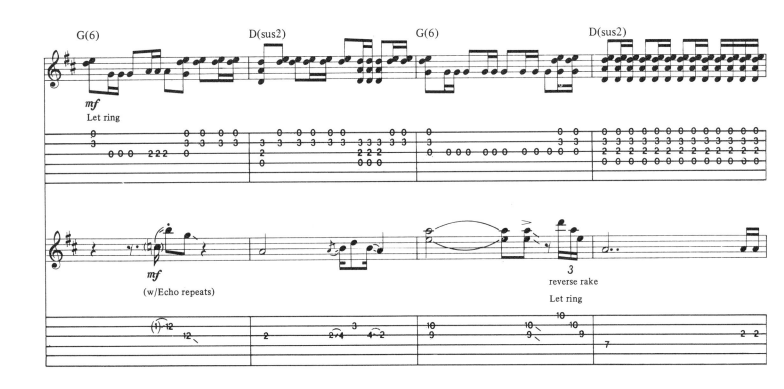

1st Verse (Gtr. II continues ad lib sound effects w/echo*)
Rhy. Fig. 1

know it's time to go, through the sleet and driv-ing snow, a-cross the fields

*Such as sliding up & down neck, strumming muted stg., etc.

of mourn-ing (to a) light's in the dis-tance. And you

hun-ger for the time, time to heal, de-sire time and your

w/Fill 1

earth moves be-neath your own dream land - scape

*low stgs. only
†high stgs. only

Fill 1

there so high___ (land), I'll be there___ to-night,___ to-

night.___

D9/13   Dsus2   G6/D   Dsus2

G6/9   Dsus2   D6/9   G6/9   Dsus2

O com-a way, I sing___ I say, um ha,   o com-a way o say.___ The wind___ will crack___

3rd Verse
w/Rhy. Fig. 1
G6/D   Dsus2   G6/D   Dsus2   G6/D

___ in win-ter-time,___ this bomb blast light - ning waltz.   No spo-ken words,___

                                                                w/Rhy. Fig. 2 *(2 times)* & Fill 5
Dsus2   G6/D   Dsus4/A D/A   G

___ just a scream,_____ yeah._____ Oh___

Gsus2   G   Gsus2   w/Rhy. Fig. 3
                                                Dsus2   G6/D Dsus4

oh._____ to - night,_____ we'll build a___ bridge___ a-

D   G(type 2)   w/Rhy. Fig. 3A
                                                G   Gsus2

cross the sea and land.___   See the sky,___ the burn-ing rain___ she___

Fill 5

THE UNFORGETTABLE FIRE

Words by BONO
Music by U2

Fill 3 (Strings arr. for gtr.)

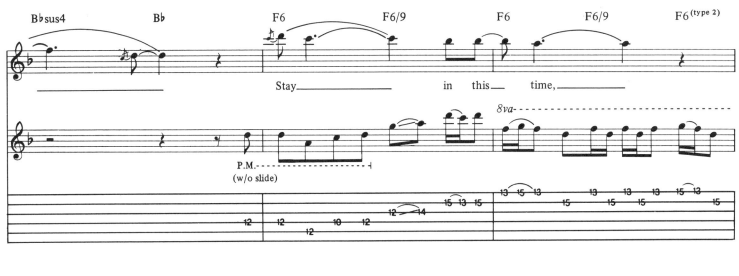

Stay_____ in this___ time,___

stay to - night___ in a lie, I'm on - ly ask -

ing but___ I, I think you know.___

Come on, take___ me a - way,___

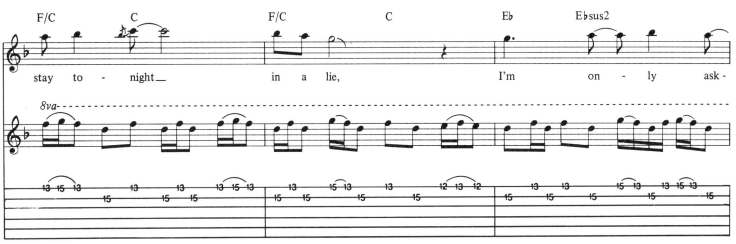

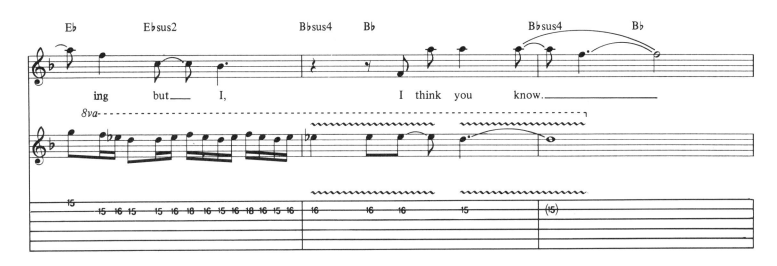

come on, take___ me a-way, come on, take___ me home,___

home___ a - gain.___

GLORIA

Words by BONO
Music by U2

*Snap pizzicato ("snap" stg. against fretboard)

BAD

Words by BONO
Music by U2

...I'm   not   sleep - ing,___ *etc.*

If   you   should ask   *etc.*

I WILL FOLLOW

Words by BONO
Music by U2

*E Mixolydian (E, F♯, G♯, A, B, C♯, D)   †Chords derived from bass figure.

I was on the out - side, *etc.*

I was on the in-

side, *etc.*

Chorus

If you walk a-way, walk a-way, *etc.*

walk   a - way, walk   a - way, *etc.*

NEW YEARS DAY

Words by BONO
Music by U2

OCTOBER

Words by BONO
Music by U2

PRIDE
(IN THE NAME OF LOVE)

Words by BONO
Music by U2

Play 3 times and fade

112

SUNDAY BLOODY SUNDAY

Words by BONO
Music by U2

3rd Verse

(*2nd, 3rd, 4th times:* Bm   D   G(6))

And the bat-tle's just— be-gun,—*etc.*

Chorus

Sun - day,— blood - y Sun - day, ————— *etc.*

How long,—*etc.*

Sustain notes

sim.

A SORT OF HOMECOMING

Words by BONO
Music by U2

O som - a way o com-

etc.

...heart   beats   so   slow, *etc.*

THE UNFORGETTABLE FIRE

Words by BONO
Music by U2

*Snap pizzicato ("snap" stg. against fretboard).

SURRENDER

Words by BONO
Music by U2

3rd Verse
E

Oh, — the cit - y's a - fire.

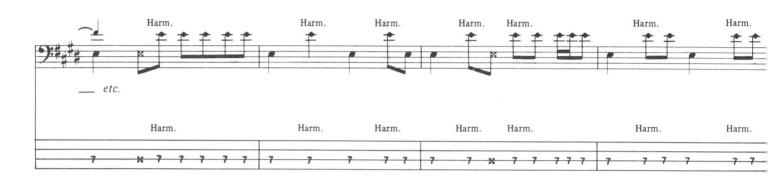

etc.

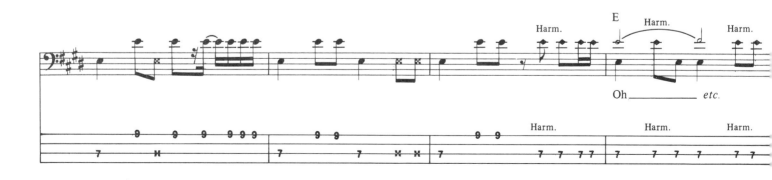

E

Oh_____ _etc._

Pa - pa sing my sing my sing my

song, *etc.*

11/93(16615)